CAUTION:

Change is difficult. Change takes time.

BUILDING WORSHIP BRIDGES

The Workbook

The Complete Construction Manual for Building Your Worship Bridges

Cathy Townley

Kay Kotan

Bishop Robert Farr

Market Square BOOKS

Building Worship Bridges: The Workbook
The Complete Construction Manual for Building Your Worship Bridges

©2017 Cathy Townley, Kay Kotan, & Bishop Robert Farr
books@marketsquarebooks.com
P.O. Box 23664 Knoxville, Tennessee 37933

ISBN: 978-0-9987546-8-0

Printed and Bound in the United States of America

Table of Contents

Introduction

This workbook is a companion to the book, Building Worship Bridges. Without the book as your guide, this construction manual (workbook) will not make sense. The workbook offers the same order of the book so it will be easy to follow along. Refer back as often as needed to the book Building Worship Bridges to help you best utilize this workbook, to get the most out of your learning and application.

Take some time to read the information in the book and then come to the workbook for reflection questions (individually and as a team), discussions, evaluation, and creating action steps for building or redesigning your worship bridge. Optimal learning comes through application, so please do take the time to both read the book and to apply your learning through the information and exercises offered in this workbook.

Caution: Be patient with yourself, your team, and your church. Change is difficult. Change takes time. Some people will be on board for changes right away. Other folks will take longer to come along. Yet other folks will choose not to move along at all. Expect all three groups and manage the transitions carefully with grace and love.

When you see the symbol below, you will know it is an opportunity for action. It is construction time! It might be a question, an evaluation, or a resource to consider. Look for this symbol for opportunities to engage your mind, conversation with others, and developing action steps to construct or redesign your worship bridge.

Part One

Bridging the
Worship Gap

Chapter One

Disastrous Bridge Collapses

After reading Chapter One, it is time to do some evaluating. Let us first look at the scripture offered in the Foreword for your reflection and discussion:

> *That day about three thousand took him at his word, were baptized and were signed up. They committed themselves to the teaching of the apostles, the life together, the common meal, and the prayers.*
> *Every day their number grew as God added those who were saved.*
>
> **Acts 2:42, 47** (MSG)

Study the scripture above. How does it speak to you about your expectations of worship? Compare your thoughts with others on your team. Now compare scriptural expectations of worship and the worship service as it stands in your church today. Record your thoughts below:

Take a look in the book at the Six Fundamentals of Bridge Design in Chapter One. Make sure you understand each of these fundamentals fully. Next, evaluate each specific fundamental in your current worship service. Which fundamentals are structurally sound in your worship service that help your service function as a bridge, and which ones are not? Evaluate individually and then evaluate with your team. Record your evaluations on the following page:

The Footings = Missional Focus

The Piers = Discipleship

The Trusses = Worship Elements

The Gusset Plates = Missional Worship

Floor Beams and Stringers = Quality and Transformation

The Roadway = Worship Journey

Chapter Two _____

Grow Healthy Churches to Build Worship Bridges

This chapter explores what it means to be a healthy church. Only healthy churches can build healthy and structurally sound worship bridges. We will begin to explore and question what it takes to be a healthy church. We will also evaluate and provide some guiding questions which will allow you to explore the healthiness and structural soundness of your church.

Inwardly or Outwardly Focused

Let us first explore the meaning of an inwardly focused church and then an outwardly focused church. Using the concepts from Chapter Two in the book, describe each. Share and compare your answers with the team's answers. Next evaluate how inwardly or outwardly focused your church is. Challenge: Consider this from the respect of not the church's intentions, but consider it based on its effectiveness in reach new people.

Define an inwardly focused church:

Define an outwardly focused church:

Evaluate your church on the above:

Cultural vs Countercultural

Review the explanation of cultural and countercultural in the book. What sticks out for you in your reading? You guessed it. It is now time to define each and evaluate your church. Do so first individually and then compare your thoughts with the team.

Define cultural:

Define countercultural:

What shifts would be necessary for your church who is counter-cultural to reach the cultural?

Who is Your Neighbor

Before we can reach our neighbor, we first need to know who our neighbor is. Spend some time running some demographics (i.e., Mission Insite), doing community assessments, speaking to community leaders, and getting to know your neighborhood. Before we can build a bridge, we must first clearly understand the two entities we are trying to connect with one another by the bridge. Through the questions below, begin to explore who is your neighbor. Caution: Please make no assumptions. Many times we "think" we know who our neighbor is, but we only know them through our selective church lens. Second caution: Sometimes churches name their neighborhoods based on where people are coming from who now attend. Do not get caught in this trap. We often have attenders who once lived in the church's neighborhood, but no longer do. They commute into the church. In addition, we often believe that if we name our mission field as large as possible, we will attract more people. The larger the mission field, usually the more diverse the demographics and mosaic types are. By tightly defining the mission field, we are more accurately able to reach the people across the street and down the block. God planted your church in that mission field to serve that mission field..

Interview a minimum of three community leaders. Have each team member do the same interviewing different leaders. Share your learnings from these conversations. Ask these questions for starters: What are the greatest needs of the community? How can the church be helpful? What is the reputation of the church in the community?

Three Greatest Need of Your Community:

1.

2.

3.

How can the church be helpful?

1.

2.

3.

What is the church's reputation?

Technical and Adaptive Change

Review the information and descriptions around both technical and adaptive change. Define each below and discuss them with your team. Ensure you have a comprehensive understanding of each before moving further into constructing or redesigning your worship bridge. This is a very important concept to understand and adopt.

Define technical change:

Define adaptive change:

Describe times when your church has gone through each type of change. How did it go? What was the outcome? What worked well? What did not work well? What was learned as a result of the change?

Chapter Three _____

A Construction Manual

As you begin to prepare for construction, it is important to ensure we know the construction principles, what type of workers we will need for the project, and what type of specialty tools might be needed for the job. This chapter helps you prepare for the construction project ahead.

Review the Ten Construction Principles in your book. Note which principle represents a technical change and which ones are adaptive. Study the list.

The Ten Construction Principles

1. Tell God's Story (technical)

2. Tell Your Story (adaptive)

3. Pay Attention to First Impressions (technical)

4. Pay Attention to Quality (adaptive)

5. Enliven the First Ten Minutes (technical)

6. Enliven Spiritual Practices (adaptive)

7. Strengthen the Ending (technical)

8. Strengthen Design Processes (adaptive)

9. Run Transitions (technical)

10. Run the Race (adaptive)

First individually and then as a team, explore the definitions of each principle. Next, evaluate each principle on how effectively your church is currently practicing the principle. Record your answers below.

1.

2.

3.

4.

5.

6.

7.

8.

9.

10.

Construction Workers

Think about your construction workers. Who is already on the team? Who is missing? Study the list and types of construction workers recommended for Building Worship Bridges. Begin a list below of what workers are already on the job site and list those workers that still need to be recruited. Make sure you build a team covering all the different needs for the various jobs of Building Worship Bridges.

Workers Already on Site	Type of Worker
1.	
2.	
3.	
4.	
5.	
6.	
7.	
8.	
9.	
10.	

Workers Already on Site	Type of Worker
1.	
2.	
3.	
4.	
5.	
6.	
7.	

8.

9.

10.

Accelerating and Decelerating Church

As introduced in the book, we are offering a comparison of Accelerating Church and Decelerating Church. The purpose of this comparison is to allow you insights into the deeper DNA of the two types of churches. Refer often to the chart below to help keep you on track of Building Worship Bridges to reach new people.

ACCELERATING CHURCH	DECELERATING CHURCH
Multiplying Small Groups	Already one big small group
Baptisms of adults and kids	A few infant baptisms
Lots of kids around	Aging population, not many kids
Good reputation in town	No reputation, no visibility
Makes new disciples	No new people
Develops leaders	Pastor does most things
Encourages transformation	Bland depiction of Jesus

Take a look at the chart above. Identify which descriptors represent your church. Share your reflections with your team and discuss. Record your insights below.

Terminology and Concepts

Familiarize yourself with the terminology and concepts towards the end of Chapter Three. Discuss which terms are new to your church vocabulary. How will you introduce this terminology and concepts to your team and your church? Record your plan below for doing so:

Identify which terminology and concepts are new to your team and your church. Then describe your plan for sharing new terminology and concepts with your team and church.

Chapter Four _____

Completing Construction

You are now beginning to move from gathering tools and a construction team into design stages. Ensure your team is recruited, all the tools are acquired, and everyone knows the principles and concepts for Building Worship Bridges. There are two other items for your consideration. Take a look below and explore the answers with your team.

Construction Deadline

As you begin to consider your worship bridge design, what is your construction deadline? Discuss two timeframes: 1. The design stage; 2. The construction stage

Consider your answers individually and then discuss as a team. What are the construction deadlines for each?

Design:

Construction:

Who will be held accountable for these deadlines? Why? How?

Noteworthy Design

Each bridge is unique in its design. How will your worship bridge be noted in your community? What will be its unique features? How will it stand out? How will your worship bridge truly bridge the church and the community? Discuss these questions with your team. Record your noteworthy design description below.

Noteworthy Design Description of your worship bridge:

Part Two

Five Phases of Building Worship Bridges

PART TWO, BUILDING WORSHIP BRIDGES	PART TWO, THE WORKBOOK
CHAPTER FIVE: Worship	PHASE ONE: Worship Orders that Tell Everyone's Story
CHAPTER SIX: Hospitality	PHASE TWO: How to Make Music a Hospitality-Wow
CHAPTER SEVEN: Praise	PHASE THREE: Using Technology to Energize the Worship Service
CHAPTER EIGHT: Discipleship	PHASE FOUR: Deepening Discipleship through the Worship Design and Sermon Writing Teams
CHAPTER NINE: Artistry	PHASE FIVE: Transitioning In, Within and Out of the Worship Service with Art and Passion

The chart above helps you match which chapter in the Workbook goes with which chapter in Part Two of *Building Worship Bridges* book.

Phase One: Worship _____

Creating Worship Orders
that Tell Everyone's Story

We left the discussion in Chapter Five of the book Building Worship Bridges, looking for a place to insert your story in the worship service. To find that place, we need a discussion about the worship order. In many existing services, the order has become dry, dusty and disconnected from any real experience of Jesus. In many new services, we find ourselves putting the worship service together in a way that is reminiscent of the churches in which we grew up with formats that date all the way back to 1950. Decelerating Church will throw this week's components of the plug and play service on the desk of the admin on Friday morning. The admin cuts and pastes from last week's service. We have missed a valuable opportunity – to innovate in our worship services. Creativity in worship design has the potential to bring more people to the new experience.[1]

We start the discussion with the basic worship pattern which you use no matter who you are or what style of worship you offer — from "traditional" to "contemporary" and whether you recognize that pattern, or not:

- The Gathering: the time before the service as people enter into the building

- The Praise: the start of the service itself, when we sing our praises to God

---

[1] We would like to share a quote from the Hartford Study of Religion Research, in which we learn of the con-nection between innovation in worship design and church growth: "What-ever a congregation's sense of inno-vation in worship, one thing has remained constant over our fifteen years of surveys—namely the strong rela-tionship that changing worship has to both growth and spiritual vitality... One of the reasons for this is the rela-tionship between innovative worship and distinguishing oneself from other congregations in one's community. Such differentiation, as previously noted in regard to Figure 12, provides a notable boost in growth." The Hart-ford Study of Religion Research, http://hirr.hartsem.edu/American-Con-gregations-2015.pdf

- The Proclamation: The Word of God

- The Response: to the Word of God

- The Dismissal: sending worshipers back out to our own lives (across the worship bridge and into the mission field, on our worship journey!)

This pattern is a simplified version of what you will find in the front of most of our denominational hymnals. It is a logical sequence of how people experience God in a public gathering. It is still useful even for our present-day services.

The bigger question is: what goes under each heading? While we, the authors, like and agree with the basic sequence of flow, we might actually differ with what your denominational hymnal says about what goes under which heading. We will be rethinking each part of the service to construct a worship bridge with a missional worship service. We will be evaluating the behaviors and attitudes that encourage story-telling during the worship service from everyone who is present there including God, leaders, regulars, new people and those not yet there.

The Three Worship Styles

Regardless of what specific items you insert under each category of the basic worship flow, most worship boils down to three worship formats:

- *Spoken-liturgy-driven.* Some might call this "traditional" or "classic" worship. There is a strong presence of spoken liturgy, creeds, responsive readings, all of which sometimes revolve around the Common Lectionary, even simply what we know as traditional liturgy.

- *Live-band-led.* Many might call this "contemporary" worship. The liturgy is in the music; it is not spoken word liturgy like above. What constitutes the live band is a variable from church to church, and often dependent upon what the mission field will bear.

- *Hybrid.* This is spoken-liturgy worship led by a live band, or sometimes a choir led service that incorporates high tech and electronics. The current terminology is Ancient Future worship; when both spoken-liturgy and band-led are somehow woven together.

COMPARING TWO COMMONLY FOUND WORSHIP ORDERS

SPOKEN – LITURGY - DRIVEN	LIVE - BAND DRIVEN
Announcements	Two to Three songs, may include spontaneous prayer
Call to worship	Welcome and Announcements
Opening hymn	Offering sometimes here
Prayer of Confession	
Congregational hymn	
Joys and concerns	
Passing the Peace	Passing the Peace
Children's sermon	Children's sermon
Choir Anthem	Music
Scripture	Offering sometimes here
Sermon	Scripture and sermon
Pastoral prayers	
Offering, Doxology	
Closing Hymn	Closing Song
Benediction and Dismissal	Benediction and Dismissal

CAUTION!!

We have tried to depict the most common worship orders we see. These are not the worship orders that reflect our biases about services that truly flow well and are the most engaging for persons in seats. As you proceed through the workbook, we will work as a team with you to put an entirely new service together in each of the formats we have identified: spoken-liturgy-driven; live-band-led; ancient-future hybrid. Even when we have shown you our preference for a strong worship service order, there can be variations.

How do you see your service in comparison to the chart above?

Insert your current worship order into the left-hand side of the chart. Then insert either the Liturgy-Driven order from the chart above or the Live-Band-Led order from the chart above into the right hand side of the chart. This will be your starting point for making changes moving forward.

YOUR SERVICE	THE LIVE-BAND OR SPOKEN-LITURGY MODEL

Tell Your Story to Change Your Church's Culture

Lay a foundation for adaptive change in your worship service immediately without waiting for permission to do so! Begin to tell your worship story publicly. You will need the worship order in front of you to do so. We will look at the order to find out where your story fits best. If you are wondering why this is important, return to Building Worship Bridges, Adaptive Construction Principle #1. The ethos of change seeps in when you authentically confess your own journey with God in the public gathering. None of us who are spiritual leaders need permission to share something about our own journeys publicly. Although if you are not the lead pastor, you may want to give him or her a heads-up!

To tell your story effectively using words, remember the following principles:

- Keep it to less than one minute.
- Prepare it ahead of time or offer a short sound bite spontaneously.
- Do not go too deep or share too much emotion.
- Make sure it connects to the topic or theme of the day; in other words, different snippets with different days and worship themes.
- Make it personal enough to show that God is real to you.
- Share truths about God as you understand them.

Below are some charts that show where various upfront leaders may want to say something about their spiritual journey during the public gathering. Our premise is that something happened to the upfront leader on the way to worship or perhaps a few days before and it is so compelling he or she needs to share it publicly. The public sharing, when done appropriately (without neediness, but instead with the confidence of the worship journey undergirding the words) has the potential to connect with persons in seats. The public connection during worship creates community, a sense of belonging, and an awareness that we are all on a worship journey. Persons in seats also have an opportunity to see how God is in their own lives when they connect with the upfront worship leader's public story telling.

TELL YOUR STORY IN SOUND-BITES
IN A SPOKEN-LITURGY-DRIVEN MODEL, Chart One

	If you're a pastor	If you're a liturgist	what might you say...
Announcements	make statement at the end, before the call to worship, as a transition		*This morning I had a new experience. I asked God to be present. I may have lost my way on asking God in. It felt so good to do it and yet so hard to see that I might have not been as open to God as I should be. Maybe you're struggling with that too. Let's all ask God in...*
Call to worship	make statement before you start call to worship, as a transition from announcements		*same as above*
Reading Scripture		make statement before reading scripture	*This morning I was feeling pretty disconnected from God. So I asked God to be present today, and I definitely felt God's presence. It was an eye opener for me, how easy it is to get disconnected from God. But I don't want to go through the motions. How about you? Maybe this scripture passage will speak to us.*
Sermon	make statement anywhere it seems to fit		*Same as in announcements or scripture, or both.*

TELL YOUR STORY IN SOUND-BITES IN A SPOKEN-LITUGY-DRIVEN MODEL
Chart Two (Featuring different upfront worship leader roles than in Chart #One)

	If you're a choir director	if you're a soloist	what might you say...
Anthem	make statement before the anthem		*This morning I was praying on my way to church and wondered if I always ask God to be present as we sing our anthem. So I asked! And I felt it! I hope you feel God's presence as we sing.*
Special music		make statement before you sing	*I was praying this morning that God would be real to me and to you as I sing. I hope you sense God's presence now.*

TELL YOUR STORY IN SOUND-BITES IN A LIVE-BAND-LED MODEL
Chart Three

WHERE	WHAT YOU COULD SAY
Before the third song, while music is playing, especially if you are the lead musician.	*I had an unusual experience this morning. It's going to sound funny, because I'm sure you would expect me to do this a lot. But I haven't always. This morning I asked God to be present. Why I haven't been doing that, well, that's another question. Anyway, I liked it, and I really do feel God is present right now. I hope you do too.*
After the welcome, before the video	*Something similar to above*
Before scripture or during the message, especially if you are the preacher	*Something similar to above*

In the charts above, notice the different upfront leaders that are represented who might speak in different places depending on their role. What they say may not be that different from each other, however! As we said in the main book, hearts influence hearts. Share your heart!

TEAM DISCUSSION QUESTIONS AND ACTION ITEMS

Make some notes below about some things that have happened this week between you and God or some things you wish would have happened.

If you were going to speak publicly about the ideas above, what would you say?

Where in the service would you share your heart about God this week? Make a commitment to who will share and where to share it:

Practice what you are going to share in front of your team. Be sure to time it to ensure it is less than one minute!

Phase Two: Hospitality _____

Making Music a Hospitality Wow

The most important thing you can do to help people connect at your church is to develop a relationship with them – to share stories! When it comes to music, style is very important; but the quality of the music is more important, because of relationship development. The quality of your music tells the most important story about your church; it tells whether you are all in and whether you really want your guest there. The role of pastors in raising the bar for quality is critical, as we described in Adaptive Construction Principle #2. Remember: quality represents the floor beams of your worship bridge.

Consider this chart to help you begin your process toward increasing the quality quotient in your church.

STEPS TO RAISE QUALITY

	Step One	Step Two	Step Three	Step Four
Lead Pastor, when it is time to talk with paid or non-paid staff about improving quality	Prays for God to be present in all conversations. Develops personal intercessors.	Shares personal testimony during worship about mission and how God is changing "my" heart. Has a conversation with the council chair. Shares heart again. Works out a plan for addressing quality issues and other items among paid and non-paid staff	Continues talking about mission and God's activity during the worship service – perhaps a sermon series on mission. Listens for affirmation. Takes the affirmer out for coffee to find out more about what they heard and how God is at work in them.	Begins the process of talking with paid and non-paid staff about mission. Work with council chair to rewrite job descriptions to reflect missional growth of leader.
Choir Director or other up front worship leader	Talks with Senior pastor about what he or she sees that needs changing	Follow steps two through four, with participation and guidance of the lead pastor		

27

Raising the bar on quality helps you build relationships with new people, which is your primary purpose as worship leaders. When your guest likes you but your music is not their style, they can get past the style if the music is executed well: not sour, free of too many mistakes, and filled with passion for the music and the worship. If your music seems cheesy – even if it is stylistically like what they hear at the gym – it will not matter if you are their BFF (Best Friend Forever). They will not be back. We hope that doesn't impact your friendship, too!

Ten Steps for Improvement: Live Band-Led

In considering live-band-led worship, we must think through what musical instruments and vocals will most likely be relevant to your mission field. We must also consider the available talent that can execute with quality and be open to continual transformation, including improving performance. Remember: quality and transformation are the floor beams and stringers of your worship bridge. The most common band is a rhythm section of guitars (acoustic and electric), bass, drums and sometimes keyboard. These are most common because more people play guitars and keys than other instruments. CAUTION: Do not limit yourself to the common. Intentionally create the music experience that intersects relevance in the mission field and the gifts of your church. The bottom line, friends: whatever the appropriate selection of music, try your best to emulate the music live that you have heard on the original recording by the professional artist of the music you are using.

Below you will find the Ten Steps for a live-band-led worship experience to start or improve your existing process and music:

1. Hire a worship leader or recruit a competent volunteer.

The lead vocal during the service is called a "worship leader." He or she is a Christian who agrees with reaching more people through your worship service; who likes the music of your mission field, who is a cultural fit with your mission field, and who can play and sing the music of your mission field. We recommend hiring a full or part time worship leader if possible; if you cannot hire, start the position with a volunteer.

Behind the pastor, this may be the most important position in the church, even more important than the youth director. The worship leader is a spiritual leader for your congregation in the public gathering through music and the arts. The right one will grow the worship arts ministry. He or she will mentor, train, coach, develop and recruit musicians and perhaps even other expressions and disciplines in the worship arts ministry.

Hiring a worship leader will cost you money; but it is one of the few expenses in all the suggestions we are making in this section. The right hire pays for themselves. Check with Accelerating Church in your area to get a feel for pay scale.

If you hire or appoint the right person, he or she may not even need to read this section. If you hire the wrong person, he or she can divide your church. When you have "artistic differences" or other areas of conflict, it could be the end of the relationship. If the worship leader decides to leave, or you decide to let this person go, he or she may be angry enough to take people with. The number may be significant, since worship leaders draw people to themselves. Offset danger when you find a person who is both called to and gifted for this ministry. Be sure your candidate does not feel he or she has all the answers already. The right candidate understands and agrees with Building Worship Bridges, as a concept, and in practice.

2. Reconfigure the Band
In the 80's, we used to have a line of singers across the front of the altar or stage with the band behind them. Every singer

29

held their own microphone. We called this the praise team and the praise band. That is so 80's!!

Keep in mind the suggestions from the paragraph above that introduces this section. Allow us to offer a description of what we most often see in growing churches. Current-style lead-vocal worship leaders play a lead instrument, usually guitar but sometimes keys. The band is usually drums, bass and one or two guitars and sometimes keys. Most instrumentalists sing backup so there are not many individual singers. It is a leaner look and easier to know who to follow.

Your upfront band configuration would look something like this:

x-bass   x-drums

x-back up vocal

x-lead   x-vocal / instrumental

3. Stop (doing so much) Talking

In the 80's, it used to be that the worship leader did a lot of talking. Today, not so much. At Accelerating Church, the music is the worship leader. Reconsider the band-led style:

BAND –LED STYLE
Two to three songs, perhaps with spontaneous prayer and a short sound-bite of personal testimony by the worship leader
Welcome and invitation

The beginning of the service is all music and music is the bridge between songs. Spoken worship leadership occurs spontaneously in short, contextual sound-bites with music in the background. Reduced verbiage is a function of group dynamics. The larger the group, the greater the need to keep the music and flow moving. If the worship leader doth-go- on with spoken words, you

30

will be standing and wondering when it is going to be over. Too much talking by upfront leaders is a disconnect.

4. Create a covenant

A worship covenant is an agreement that helps the worship leader and worship arts participants work together. It helps you raise the bar on quality because it raises the bar on commitment. Those who are committed to the process have bought into the work it takes to build a worship bridge. The covenant addresses both the role and behaviors of the leader and the rest of the band and singers. The most important item in a covenant is the agreement to come to practices prepared. Worship bridges fail without efficiency.

Preparation expectations:
- Musicians know their parts before they get there.
- The leader will have identified each part for each musician in a professionally produced recording the leader sends to each participant at least a week ahead of the practice, if not two.

Additional covenantal values:
- Being on time to practices.
- Length of practice (usually 90 minutes)
- Number of practices
- Number of times you are scheduled to perform (no more than 3x per month per person)

The worship leader has the responsibility to build community with the band and singers. Likewise, the band and singers have the expectation to be part of a community. For everyone (leaders, band and singers alike) being part of the community includes practicing spiritual disciplines and the desire to grow as a Christ-follower. How the leader accomplishes this is up to the leader, but it cannot be ignored or left to chance.

5. Strategize with music selection

The live-band-led style requires that you help your band learn a lot of music. We recommend managing the number of songs to improve performance. Reduce the number of musicians from the beginning of a worship service to the end of that service so that only the most proficient musicians will learn all the songs and those that need more work can be responsible for learning fewer songs.

Organize the amount of music you learn in a year overall. To get started, learn:

- Twelve up-beat songs for the opening song
- Twenty-four mellower to slow songs for the second and third songs
- Add in one new opening song and one new second song per month after about six months
- Learn hymns and traditional music (done in your style) for Advent, Christmas and Easter

6. Make practices efficient

Good musicians want a focused practice. Start the practice with some type of spiritual discussion and prayer, for about 10 minutes. The rest of the practice is now hard-work. Keep in mind: the whole group is only going to learn the first three songs. If there are additional songs with smaller configurations of musicians, you can practice those at another time. You might also save a portion of the practice time for the smaller configurations, after you release the others. There are numerous ways to run an efficient practice. Here is one way:

- Start by listening to the recording of the first song you're going to do this Sunday
- Point out what you want to make sure happens

- Do one run through
- Address rough spots individually; those not having to address their part listen and wait
- Listen for vocals and tuning
- Call out whoever is sharp, flat, or untuned (instruments) with grace; eliminate harmony if too hard to make work this week
- Repeat with the next song
- If you have three songs, run each song for about 20 minutes
- Dedicate the remainder of the practices (at least 20 minutes) to running transitions between songs (if you have a band-driven service) or anywhere in the service you are transitioning music into something else

SHOUT OUT: The last item on this list is SUPER IMPORTANT! Musical transitions are one of the most important things you will address to make the worship service flow. They are bridges within the service. More on this topic later.

7. Use recorded music

Many of us who are music purists under-rate the value of using already recorded music in the service. Your guest will not mind as much as you do. In our current culture, people are used to watching videos, especially music videos. If you are just starting out or trying to get a band up to speed that has been struggling, reduce the number of live songs and replace a couple with music videos:

- Search YouTube for contemporary Christian music videos. There are free ways to download videos that do not cause copyright problems for your church. The artists in the video are the worship leaders. Superimpose song lyrics on the video in a movie editing software so the congregation can sing along. The live worship leader can be in front of the congregation, too.

- Google "purchasing music videos" to find numerous companies that sell music videos for your use in worship.
- Make your own video with Power Point or Keynote. Embed the full recorded song in the slide show and insert the lyrics on the slide too. Your own, live, up-front worship leader can sing along and lead the congregation as the worship band in the professional, studio-produced recording is playing the song for everyone to sing along with.

PERSONAL NOTE: Cathy uses this approach in her worship seminars with highly positive results. The participation and experience of persons in seats is very powerful, in part because there are no mistakes by the musicians! Many church musicians turn up their noses at the concept, until they experience it. If you do not have a good band or you are working on developing one, use the fully produced studio recording as your band. It works!

8. MUST-HAVES

Develop a sound

As you progress in finding music for your setting, you may land upon a style that suits you. There is value in having an identifiable sound. The tighter your band gets, the more of a sound you will have.

Establish an audition process

Run auditions to find people that have enough musical skill that want to get better and that also want to serve Jesus or at least find out more about Jesus. We believe in including marginal Christians in upfront leadership, as long as the new or searching Christian is not the primary leader. The purpose of the audition is to weed out those persons that think they are better than they are. No show-boating allowed.

Schedule musicians

Use a scheduling tool like Planning Center On-Line (PCO) for managing volunteers.

Raise up disciples

Find a way to help your people grow spiritually without adding too much time to participation schedules. Musicians are already involved in an affinity group (music)!

Expand your musical horizons

Listen to secular music and incorporate the more spiritual songs into worship.

Learn loops

A "loop" is a few measures or bars of musical accompaniment that you can play from a recording while your band is playing live. There is a significant learning curve associated with loops. It is worth your time to figure out how they work.

9. Update your marquee and your website

When you are ready, put the following on your marquee and on your website:

LIVE-BAND SERVICE at __(time)__.

People will know what you are talking about. Do not use the language "contemporary" worship. It's meaningless to guests and church regulars alike.

10. Improve technology

See the next chapter.

Ten Steps for Improvement: Traditional

Below you will find the ten steps for a traditional style service between 50 and 200 in worship, or to improve music in a struggling traditional service (when overall attendance is above 200).

We (the authors) have never been choir directors. Bishop Farr and Cathy have both led services or churches in which we have helped a traditional service become more current. All the authors have had enough exposure to transformational churches and new start environments to be able to tell you what usually works to build bridges. This discussion is geared to smaller churches, and also to larger churches with smaller, struggling traditional worship services. We are referring to traditional services as "choir led" in this segment devoted to music.

1. Recruit

Every music ministry in every church should be growing, even in choir-led services. Read Ken Callahan's oldie-but-goodie-gem-of-a-book, Dynamic Worship.[2] There is a chapter on the role of the choir director in a traditional church. Follow that. In a Decelerating Church, choir directors can feel they have gone as far as they can go in getting new people. We feel your pain. It is still the choir director's job to grow the ministry. Suggestions below will help you fulfill your calling to recruit and add more people.

2. Change your musical style

Too many churches use choir music that is very difficult for a choir to sing, particularly an older choir. And in most churches, most choir members have a lot of gray hair. Listening to the choir sing a difficult song in which the soprano is exposed with a vibrato as wide as a mountain peak is high is not hospitable. We are sorry if that stings.

[2] Dynamic Worship, ibid (Building Worship Bridges)

We have noticed that some choirs have moved to an easier listening praise style, using classic praise songs from throughout the decades. Arrangements abound. Google *"Choir Arrangements of Praise Songs."*

3a. Reduce the number of times the choir sings, or the number of times each person sings

It is a conundrum as to why a church with a choir of five to ten people sings every week. That is not a choir. It is an ensemble. And in most cases, it is not a very good ensemble. Consider an alternative:

- In the summer, go person to person in the congregation to get participants for a one- time Advent celebration on one Advent Sunday. Learn one to two songs.
- Make a minimum goal of doubling your regular choir participants for this event.
- Get your participants to recruit as you recruit.
- Start your practices in September. Rehearse 2x the first month, 2x the second month, and 4 times the third month
- After Advent, schedule your next date for this group to sing again.
- Schedule the ensemble 1x per month, use solos (follow #4, below) and recordings (follow #5, below.)

3b. Recruit for special events

If you have a 25 to 30 voice choir, you probably have more people than that who would love to be part of the choir infrequently. Invite them to sing for a holiday and increase your size. See item 3a, above.

4. Create an audition process

When it comes to doing special music, do not just have people sign up and do whatever they want. That gets poor results.

Create an audition system for a song you select:

- target some people you think might be able to do it well
- ask them to learn it and perform it for you
- open the audition to others you did not target
- select the best one
- tell others there is something for them down the road
- if there are any that should not be singing solos, it is okay to tell them so kindly.

5. Use recorded music

See item 6 under Live-Band-led improvements, above. Additionally, Google traditional hymns done current style to find recordings of old-hymn standards for your context. Then consider where to use recorded music in place of live, in the following chart:

SPOKEN-LITURGY DRIVEN
Announcements
Call to worship
Opening hymn*
Prayer of Confession
Congregational hymn*
Joys and concerns
Passing the Peace*
Children's sermon
Choir Anthem*
Scripture*
Sermon
Prayers of the People
Offering* and doxology
Closing hymn*
Benediction and Dismissal

Every asterisk represents a place where recorded music would fit. You do not need to use them all, but you could. Any time you already would be doing congregational music, you can make the musical accompaniment a recording. The next chart gives you a way to add a recorded song or video along with some words to say to set it up.

WORSHIP LEADING USING RECORDED MUSIC

Spoken-Liturgy Driven		
Pass the Peace*		
While your congregation is passing the peace, start the recording or the video	The music and the video will naturally draw attention back to the screen.	The upfront "live" leader can begin singing with the recording; soon everyone will be singing. Tell people to be seated when finished.
Scripture*	When the reading of scripture is done, the upfront worship leader starts the recording or video, but keeps it soft. As it is beginning, he or she says something like:	When done, the upfront live leader has people sit down as the pastor comes up to preach.
The "live" worship leader can be in his or her spot as the scripture reader is reading the passage.	Let's sing together to let God's words sing into our hearts.	

6. Arrange a contemporary song for a traditional / liturgical setting

Find current style music that you can use in a traditional setting. Maybe slow down the tempo and use just keys or guitar as accompaniment. Find chord charts on line.

7. Find the right spot and words to put the best foot forward on new music.

Look at the chart above for using recorded music to see where to include new music.

8. MUST HAVES

Raise up disciples, expand your musical horizons and learn loops
See item #8 in the Band-Led style, above.

9. Update your marquee and website

As with the Live-Band-Led service, put the following on your marquee when ready. People will know what you are talking about! Don't say "traditional" worship!

CHOIR LED SERVICE at ___(time)___.

10. Improve technology

See next chapter.

ANCIENT-FUTURE WORSHIP ORDER
Using both old hymns and new songs

Ancient / Future Order	
ANNOUNCEMENTS	Scrolling on the screen before the service, contemporary Christian music as background. CHAPTER THREE.
BELL	ANY signal that worship is about to begin
LITURGY	Host leads any ancient or modern liturgy
HYMN	Use a powerful, introductory hymn
PASSING THE PEACE	Use music to control the length; CHAPTER THREE
PRAISE SONG	Less energetic than the opening hymn
WELCOME	Host leads. See CHAPTER THREE for insight on a great welcome
VIDEO	Testimonial, or thematic
MESSAGE	Preacher may include scripture reading in the message, along with additional videos or images
INTERACTIVE PRAYER	CHAPTER FOUR
CREED	(OPTIONAL)
COMMUNION	(OPTIONAL)
OFFERING	Live or recorded music, CHAPTER FOUR
DOXOLOGY	(OPTIONAL)
CLOSING HYMN	CAN REPEAT A VERSE FROM OPENING HYMN
DISMISSAL, BENEDICTION	CHAPTER FOUR
RECORDED MUSIC	Contemporary Christian

Our primary purpose for including this chart here is to show how you can combine ancient and future styles for a welcoming, relatable and potentially powerful WOW experience. The chart above illustrates how a choir led service might incorporate

41

contemporary praise music into an existing service (without offending everyone!). NOTICE: We have moved announcements to before the service and have inserted a welcome after the Praise to create an invitational, relational environment.

TEAM QUESTIONS AND ACTION ITEMS FOR IMPROVING MUSIC

Which of the items in the above lists of instructions are most doable for you right now?

What is the timeline for making the initial changes you have identified?

What will be your stumbling blocks to making harder changes and how will you address those?

What is the timeline for making additional changes that you cannot make now but would like to make in the future?

Phase Three: Technology _____

Using Technology to Infuse Energy in the Worship Service

Chapter Seven of Building Worship Bridges ends by lifting up how technology impacts the entire service. Technology can tempt us to be cool. Instead, let us use it as it is intended: to help us tell God's story and ours in new ways. Surrender coolness! The following charts and comments will provide ideas for expanding the use of technology throughout your worship service.

GENERAL USE OF SCREENS

RETHINKING GENERAL SCREEN USAGE	IT'S INTERACTIVE
Use words on the screen for music, prayer and scripture, and occasionally during the sermon.	Increases participation for all ages.
Use a picture of the following when talking about them at any time during the service: * Mentioning someone by name. * Talking about a missional activity * Talking about a church activity	Peers influence peers.
Limit bullet points during your sermon. Use images and videos instead of words.	Increases impact.
During communion, on the screen, use: • Classic art with recorded background music • Music video with words • Recording of a song with words • Live music with images	Classic art hits our intellect as well as emotion. Video or a recording of a song with lyrics posted allows people to absorb meaning without expectation of singing. You might still hear people singing softly. Live music with images captures creativity.
Call people to action using words with images. Words might be: "Find a way to listen to your coworker this week." Image might be clip art of an ear or someone listening.	Conviction!

REMINDER: Do not forget to use your lobby screens (flat screen TV's) before and after the worship service. This is a great opportunity for connection, invitation and discipleship.

 ACTION ITEMS FOR SCREEN USAGE:

What are the top three things you can do to enhance screen usage in your church?

1.

2.

3.

What is your timeline for implementing your top three picks?

ANNOUNCEMENTS: JUST FOR US

Determine what you want to announce and make a slide for each topic. For example, let's say one topic you want to cover is that your church is going to re-purpose your church library into a coffee bar and an all-purpose room for kids to come after school and use computers. The purpose in showing the slide is to find workers to help re-purpose the room – cleaning, organizing and maybe other construction tasks. You may want to develop a slide-show sequence for this one topic. Note that your church website should go on all slides, with a dedicated page on your site for people to find out more about the topic. We have shown you how to do this in the chart on the next page:

HOW TO MAKE AN ANNOUNCEMENT-SLIDE

	CONTENTS OF THE SLIDE	RUNNING THE SLIDE
Slide one	IMAGE YOU MIGHT USE *Google "clip art for house cleaners" to find fun ideas* CAPTION FOR THAT IMAGE MIGHT SAY *Help transform the library into multi-purpose space for after school kids program*	Keep this (and all slides) on the screen long enough to absorb the content, maybe 5 seconds
Slide two	NEW picture follows of an artist's rendering of how the room will look when competed. CAPTION MIGHT SAY *Meet in the Library after worship next week. We'll feed you before you work! See more at...* Churchwebsite.com/libraryproject	You can use two slides to impart the big picture, or you can make one slide with two sides to it. Note the website with the church name and specific page on the website where people can find out about that specific project. Make communication simple and descriptive. Include a website and website page reference on every slide.

ACTION ITEM FOR ANNOUNCEMENTS:

What will it take to include announcements scrolling on the screen before the service? Consider both hardware and software, as well as preparing the congregation for this technical change.

What is your timeline for implementing scrolling announcements?

THE COUNTDOWN VIDEO. Google "countdown videos" for free ones! Use them to start your Praise Segment with strength. Organists wish that people would sit quietly during the Gathering to listen to the prelude they have worked so hard on. People will stop talking when the slides, background music and countdown video end simultaneously and the prelude begins.

HOW TO USE A COUNTDOWN VIDEO

	ACTION	COUNTDOWN VIDEO
The Gathering	Announcements / scrolling before the service starts; recorded background music is playing.	The countdown video is either part of every slide or it's a slide of its own that comes in and out of the slide-show loop. Start the countdown when you start your announcement loop, about 15 minutes before the start of the service.
The Praise	The band or the organist enter toward the end of the announcement loop, with about a minute to go. They get in their place and are ready to begin their part of the service as soon as the countdown video reaches zero.	The countdown video reaches 0. • Band-led: Music starts, leader invites people to stand, singing begins. • Spoken Liturgy: Organist begins prelude at "0". Organist transitions between Prelude and opening hymn. Organist, host or song leader can invite people to sing.

ACTION ITEM FOR COUNTDOWN VIDEO:

What will it take to include a countdown video? Consider both hardware and software, as well as preparing the congregation for this technical change.

What is your timeline for using one?

THE WELCOME AND INVITATION: JUST FOR THEM

The welcome is a transition between the Praise and the Proclamation. If done well, it will help persons in seats feel more connected to your church and the purpose of your church to make new disciples of Jesus Christ for the transformation of the world.

HOW TO DO A POWERFUL WELCOME AND INVITATION

A POWERFUL WELCOME: THE HOST IS...	OPPORTUNITY DISCIPLESHIP
... helpful. Include layout of building, including bathrooms and where to bring kids both before and during the service; safety features; website info. About 60 seconds.	Guest feels welcomed into someone else's "home."
... relational. First introduce yourself. Be warm and friendly. 30 seconds. Second, invite guests to coffee after the service to find out more about the church and have great coffee. Put up pictures of coffee area and of people connectors or greeters, telling guests to look for these people who will give them insight. Say where connectors will be. 60 seconds	Guest feels included.
...missional. What's happening in the life of the church this week that impacts the neighborhood and the mission field? What will happen next week in worship that will not happen anywhere else, to tie this week to next? Use images! 60 seconds	Guest may become curious about what mission really is. Holy Spirit stirring and discipleship thread.

ACTION ITEMS FOR WELCOME:

What will it take to do a welcome like we have described?

What is your timeline for developing a welcome (and up front hosts)?

PAPER BIBLES V DIGITAL BIBLES

They are on our phones! You can still have pew bibles; but then, when telling people to use their phone app, tell them the version to use that is the same as your pew Bible. We've got an app for that...

HOW TO USE A BIBLE APP

RETHINKING BIBLE USAGE	IT'S INTERACTIVE
When it's time for reading scripture, put the passage on the screen. Also, ask people to open their Bibles and Bible apps.	Knowing how accessible the Bible is and learning to use it electronically
Don't say: please turn off your phones. You can say, please silence your ringer, and keep your phone out to access your Bible	The ringer is the problem, not the phone.
While you're at it, encourage people to check in at your church on Face-Book.	It is an easy evangelism tool. More importantly, checking in endorses the worship experience to persons in seats. Endorsing worship helps people grow into discipleship. And that's our goal.

ACTION ITEMS FOR ENCOURAGING ELECTRONIC USE OF BIBLES

What will it take to find a Bible app for your church and encourage people to read their Bibles on their phones, especially during worship?

What is your timeline for developing communication about using electronic Bibles (and maybe paper ones, too)?

TEXTING PRAYERS

Technology can help you manage the unwieldy time of joys and concerns we see in many congregations by involving more people in the process of prayer. We do not recommend abruptly ending Joys and Concerns if you currently offer them. Instead, add more ways to include people in prayer. Texting is one way to do that.

HOW TO INCLUDE TEXTING PRAYERS INTO YOUR WORSHIP SERVICE

USING TEXTING FOR PRAYERS	IT'S INTERACTIVE
Continue to offer joys and concerns the way your congregation does it. Phase out passing the mic by having cards that ushers can collect with prayer requests on them.	While you're collecting written prayer requests, have people begin texting.
FOR PASTORAL CARE: Text prayers to a pastoral care phone number that's listed in the bulletin or on the screen.	Create a system of feedback on prayers that are sent to the pastoral care person. It is a personal, direct approach, but not anonymous. Your person is texting to that number to get a personal response from someone who can be pastorally present to them.
FOR LIVE WORSHIP INTERACTION: Text prayers live to a worship leader in the worship service or directly to a screen depending on the size of your congregation. Reassure people that no one will know who is texting, so they can say whatever is truly on their mind. Texting is anonymous.	Prayer belongs to everyone, not just the "prayer specialists" of the church like the pastor, the prayer chain or the prayer team. When we hear and see the prayer requests of the congregation in the worship service, it gives us a window into community life and it gives us the heart for real people living real life.

To text prayers anonymously in different size congregations:

- For churches under 100 in worship, acquire a phone dedicated to the purpose of receiving texts during the service. Announce that your phone has no contacts so that texting will be anonymous. Read texted prayer requests over soft music.

- For churches between 100 and 500, acquire two phones, as directed above. Jockey back and forth between readers of prayers on each phone over soft music.

- For churches over 500 in worship, text polling is the solution. Comments and prayers post right to the screen. Cathy has used this in services she has led with over 1000 in attendance. Hundreds of people post. It is very powerful. Google "text polling."[3]

ACTION ITEMS FOR TEXTING PRAYERS

What will it take to introduce prayer texting in your congregation? Consider both hardware and software, as well as preparing the congregation for this technical change.

What is your timeline for developing prayer texting?

---

[3] Cathy has learned about a phone or iPad app that assigns you a phone number. When others call it you do not receive their name. Cathy has not yet tried this app. It might be the way to go for creating an opportunity for persons in seats to share thoughts while remaining anonymous.

HIGH TECH GIVING

Hardly anyone carries cash or checks. Increase giving by going digital. You will net more even considering bank fees. Get Square (a device that connects to a cell phone) and put a Square device kiosk in the lobby for guests to give on the way out. Offer texting options for giving. Promote auto withdraw for pledges through banks. If you are worried about debt for those that use credit cards to give, teach about debt and stewardship.

HOW TO USE ELECTRONICS FOR OFFERING

RETHINKING OFFERING	IT'S INTERACTIVE
Pass the basket and give people an opportunity to text their offering, and put a kiosk with your Square device in the lobby and offer auto withdrawal	Learning to give; automated giving.

ACTION ITEMS FOR DIGITAL AND ELECTRONIC GIVING

What will it take to introduce electronic and digital giving?

What is your timeline for doing so?

INTERNET V LIVE WORSHIP

Bishop Farr likes to say: "Technology allows you to be there when you're not actually there." Internet worship is growing and has specific implications for the life of the church. Blogger and pastor Carey Neuwholf has suggested that Internet worship will be the way many new people check out the church, and that something else happens in the live and on-site setting.[4] We agree. Different forms of participation may be the key.

HOW TO ENCOURAGE PARTICIPATION IN THE LIVE-WORSHIP EXPERIENCE

Who's the Up Front Leader	Where to Encourage Participation	What the Leader Might Say
Band leader, worship leader, choir director, pastor, host, liturgist	Musicians: between songs Host: the welcome Liturgist: scripture, call to worship Pastor: message	*I'm so grateful to see your worship of God and how the Holy Spirit touches you;* *Thank you all for your worship leading* *You can close your eyes and just listen, or read along with me using your Bible app or the pew Bible* *You can read out loud with me or just consider what we are saying*

ACTION ITEMS FOR ENCOURAGING PARTICIPATION:

What will it take to encourage persons in seats to participate in different ways?

What is your timeline for doing so?

---

[4]We like blogger Carey Nieuwhof. He agrees with us! He just doesn't know us. We know him though. Check out the article: http://careynieuwhof.com/2016/01/5-disruptive-church-trends-will-rule-2016/

USING MUSIC AS A THREAD

Tie the praise section together within itself for a strong beginning. In Accelerating Church, you are just as likely to see a passing of the peace as not, with music controlling the time it takes.

HOW TO USE MUSIC AS A THREAD OF CONNECTION

SPOKEN LITURGY: TWO HYMNS	TRANSITION
Opening song or hymn begins	Congregation Stands
Opening song ends	Host in place
	Host invites into responsive reading
Responsive reading finished	Host invites hand shake / passing peace
Ten seconds into passing peace	Music begins to next hymn, words on screen
Fifteen seconds into passing peace	Choir or worship leader starts singing hymn
Second hymn finished	Host in place, asks congregation to be seated Congregation sits
Host offers personal welcome	

SPOKEN LITURGY: ONE HYMN AND REPRISE	TRANSITION
Opening song begins	Congregation Stands
Opening song ends, organist or accompanist transitions musically to next song / hymn*	Choir director acts as worship leader, along with the choir, to engage congregation
Second song / hymn complete	Host in place*
	Host invites into responsive reading
Responsive reading done	Host invites hand shake / passing peace
Ten seconds into passing peace	Organist counts to ten, then picks up the last verse of the second hymn and plays once through; choir director and choir begin singing verse, sing it once through, may need to repeat to get entire congregation singing the reprise
Reprise complete	Host in place, asks congregation to be seated Congregation sits
Host offers personal welcome	

53

LIVE BAND LED: FIRST TEN MINUTES	TRANSITION
Band starts playing	Congregation Stands
Worship leader tells people to stand as the music is playing and as they're standing	Singing begins
First song ends, worship leader uses lead instrument to begin second song	Singing begins
Second song ends, worship leader uses lead instrument to begin third song; may direct band to keep playing as he or she talks	Worship leader says something welcoming, warm, or spiritual to congregation, perhaps prays, has people pass the peace
Third song begins	Worship leader / band starts singing, people join in
Third song over, music continues softly	Worship leader prays one more time, has people be seated
Worship leader directs band to stop	Host in place, makes personal connection between music experience and congregation
Host offers personal welcome*	

ACTION ITEM FOR IMPROVING THE FLOW OF PRAISE:

What will it take to increase the use of music as a thread during the Praise?

What is your timeline for doing so?

Phase Four: Discipleship _____

Deepening Discipleship Through the Worship Design and Sermon Writing Teams

As we mentioned already in Building Worship Bridges, pastors and other creative types believe it is easier and faster to put the service together by themselves every week. Besides the fact that you will miss the discipleship connection, you will also quickly grow stale without working with others.

The worship design team

The worship design team is a group comprised of thinkers, creators, culturally aware people and good communicators that design worship with the pastor. The group helps the church fulfill the mission of encouraging worshipers to praise God during the worship service. The worship journey continues after the worship service. The design team accomplishes these tasks by lifting up current, relevant issues creatively and artistically during the service. The structure of your team is going to depend on your church's size and the pastor's personal leadership style. Effective worship design teams span a loose structure to a more organized, tighter structure; from lay driven to staff driven. Find a style that works for you as you consider one way of organizing this group. The pastor prays and discerns who to invite to be on the team. Once the team is in place, here are the next steps:

- The pastor and the team go away to work on worship themes or scripture passages for worship for the next three to six months.
- The pastor comes prepared for the retreat having already thought through where the church is headed and where God wants the church to go. He or she may have already selected scripture passages to work on for each Sunday.
- The team wrestles with the themes and comes up with

creative ways to express the themes during the service.

- The worship design team structure might look like this – see the charts below:

HOW TO ORGANIZE A WORSHIP DESIGN TEAM

Design team process	Pastor's role	Implementation
	Pastor designs themes or selects scripture or both prior to retreat, perhaps a few months before meeting with team	Pastor or worship leader or design team representative hands off themes to creative implementation team
Worship Design team goes away with pastor for half day to day and a half retreat	THREE TO SIX MONTHS OUT	A COUPLE WEEKS TO A MONTH OUT

This particular organizational structure introduces another team you could call an *implementation team*. This group functions to implement the ideas of the design team. Note that the design team does not necessarily implement any of the creative concepts they have come up with, although they might. You might organize in this way:

- A representative from the design team, or various persons in the design team, reach out to individuals in the church who have gifts and graces for creative expression.
- You will know who those people are through spiritual gift inventories and, really, fruit! Some creative people would rather not sit on a team at a retreat to come up with ideas for how to do worship. Instead they may prefer to have someone tell them what the design team is looking for and then they create it.

Thinking about the service creatively: back to the worship order!
- The creative design process may depend on your church's size and could work like this:
- Put a worship order together that is repeated weekly
- Find places in the service to approach creatively, weekly. If you are under 100 in worship, plan to do one to two

56

things creatively. If you are over 100 in worship, plan to do three or four. If you are over 250 in worship, the sky could be the limit!

- The asterisks on the chart illustrate all the areas that could be done creatively.

WORSHIP DESIGN TEAM CREATIVITY CHART

SPOKEN LITURGY CREATIVITY CHART
Announcements scroll during Gathering*
Prelude
Opening Hymn
Invitation to worship*
Passing Peace
Second hymn
Host welcome*
Video *
Choir Anthem
Scripture*
Sermon
Interactive prayer*
Offering*
Final invitation to discipleship*
Benediction, followed by postlude or recorded music

Things to notice about our chart. Regardless of whether your worship format is a spoken-liturgy style or a live-band-led style, we are asking you to consider this chart and read the comments below. We will share a chart for live-band led services, too, drawing from the same concepts as you'll find under this heading.

- *Scrolling announcements.* Some churches use the admin to put scrolling announcements together weekly – great idea if the admin has creative skills. To expand the creativity, find one or two more the admin can train. Hand off production to a new person periodically.

- *Invitation to worship.* This can be a responsive reading. If you are live-band led or ancient-future, it might be a short community reading of some kind. Sometimes the pastor might write this himself or herself. Or someone with creative writing skills can put something together based on scripture and theme.

- *Host welcome and invitation.* First, we recommend finding at least two hosts to alternate Sundays (or whatever day your worship service is). One or both might be able to do their own welcome with visuals. Sometimes the team might want to do something very different, like an original video. The team could offer the opportunity for the host to create the video or find someone else to create it.

- *Video.* If you are doing a video during the welcome, you can still do a video after the welcome as a transition to the next segment. In the 21st Century, there is room for multiple videos in one service. The video after the welcome could be a testimonial video, or a video about the scripture passage or theme. Videos are very easy to make and produce – much easier than a drama or something live. You do not have to produce them professionally; amateur videos will do. The production is not critical; the content is. That is the influence of YouTube in our Me generation.

- *Scripture.* You might consider doing something inventive with scripture, like two readers who could read the passage like a drama; or one person who memorizes the passage and "performs" it, as people read along on the screen. Do those things infrequently. Keep scripture short, and have the congregation read it out loud with you a couple times. That is impactful. You can do that most weeks.

- *Interactive prayer (discipleship thread)* We have identified texting prayers as a way to involve more people. You can do that most weeks. We will give you more tips on how to tie texting prayers to the sermon (as a discipleship thread) in our charts at the end of this chapter. Sometimes you may wish to do stations of the cross, or prayer at the altar with prayer partners that come out of the prayer team. That would mean that you would have two prayer partners at the altar and invite people forward for prayer and anointing. This live, interactive type of prayer works best when it is after the service is over because then people do not have to walk back to their seats with everyone staring at them!

- *Offering (discipleship thread).* In our charts, we have given some ideas about how to do offering using recorded music instead of live music. It takes more production to put a recorded song together with visuals or images on the screen, but it is worth doing that sometimes. It can be very powerful, especially if you have tied the song and the visuals to the pastor's theme.

- *Final invitation to discipleship / dismissal.* You might offer an assignment to people of what you want them to do this week (and tie that to what you are doing next week). The pastor can do this himself or herself or hand it off to a creative type on the implementation or design team.

- *Music.* The band leader or choir director probably will pick the music and hymns to go with the themes. Paid or volunteer staff might be a regular part of the design retreats so that they can have a jump start on selecting appropriate music.

- *Keep it simple.* We have listed several areas of the worship service to do creatively.

  CAVEAT: Do not think you must do them all! Managed creativity is a beautiful thing in worship design. DO NOT WEAR YOUR PEOPLE OUT! Act your size and ability for maximum results.

- *Plug and play.* We have much maligned this approach to

worship. It is not all bad. When you develop design and implementation teams and when you keep creativity manageable, the rest of the service can indeed be plug and play.

LIVE-BAND CREATIVITY CHART

LIVE BAND-LED CREATIVITY CHART
Announcements scroll during the Gathering*
Three praise songs
Video (testimony)*
Welcome begins*
Video (thematic) and offering*
Sermon, with prayer, texting, visuals woven in
Assignment, benediction, dismissal*
Recorded music

Things to notice about the live-band creativity chart

The live-band led service commonly ends with the sermon. Therefore, we have inserted the offering before the sermon, though it can go after the sermon if you prefer. We have inserted prayer into the sermon time. That is our bias since so many churches that are doing live-band led have no real interaction with persons in seats. Some churches are still reaching their mission field when they have a talking-head sermon if the preacher is exceptionally good. But you might be surprised at how a church that has good music and good preaching still does not grow.

We have already introduced this topic; we repeat it here because it is relevant to worship design and discipleship. We can surmise a couple reasons that the reason churches do not grow when they have good music and preaching. Maybe it is because their style does not suit the mission field. Perhaps there is conflict in the church. Or maybe it is because there is no reason for people to return to the live setting. Using creativity to connect with persons in seats gives them a possible reason to return. We cannot overlook creativity and personal connections.

The sermon writing team

It is certainly apparent to you that we did not include an asterisk by the sermon in either of our two charts above. It is not as effective to open the doorway to sermon creativity with the design team. We need a sermon writing team for that!

The cutting edge in sermon development is for the pastor to work with a group of laypersons to literally write the sermon every week based on the work of the worship design team. There are different ways to organize sermon writing teams, again based on the size of the church and style of the pastor. The growth edge for most pastors is working with someone else to write the sermon, and then – horrors! – delivering the sermon to that group (plus a few others) before delivering it to the congregation. We introduced the idea of humility already.

The lead pastor leads the way on having an unoffendable spirit. We know without a doubt that working with a sermon-writing team and getting feedback on your delivery from people who are honest with you is going to be a huge stretch for most pastors reading this book. Seventh inning...

The trend in *Accelerating Church* is to have the lead pastor preach less than 40 weeks each year. It used to be that the lead pastor was in the pulpit close to 50 weeks. Pastors that are preaching less feel their sermons have improved. During the 12 or more weeks the pastor is not in the pulpit, the church often raises up someone from the sermon writing team to be the preacher for the day. In this way, the church is raising up more communicators from within. The process of working with a sermon writing team might look like this – see chart below:

HOW TO WORK WITH A SERMON WRITING TEAM

Structure	Themes	Writing and Feedback	Scaling for Growth
	Pastor has selected two scripture passages for two weeks ahead	The preacher writes and delivers the sermon to the team	Pastor can develop another team for a different week
At least TWO on the team besides the pastor	The team wrestles with the passages to discern the theme. They give the theme to the design team for their creative interpretation throughout the service.	The delivery can be live or recorded. If recorded, the individuals on the team can listen on their own time and give feedback separately.	Teams multiply as the pastor works ahead on themes and preaching topics. Team participants can have a turn at being preacher.

Your process should scale easily as you grow. Start with two teams for maximum impact. Using our chart above, that means on week one you would work with team one for the sermon two weeks out. On week two, you work with team two for theme development for the next sermon two weeks out. You also deliver your sermon for this current week to team one for their feedback. If you have three or four teams and work ahead more than two weeks, it might be three or more weeks before the first team meets again to give feedback on the sermon they helped write.

Discipleship Threads

The main topic of this chapter is discipleship. In Building Worship Bridges, we discussed the impact of discipleship on worship design. We also introduced the idea that the worship design and sermon writing teams are going to be deeply involved in living out discipleship and implementing it in their worship design practices.

On the next page are some charts to give you an idea of how the flow will look in both worship formats we have been working with: spoken-liturgy and live-band-led. We have identified that the ending of your service begins during the Welcome. We have detailed the flow of the worship service from the welcome to the dismissal in both the spoken-liturgy and live-band models.

SPOKEN LITURGY DISCIPLESHIP THREADS CHART

FROM THE SERMON	ACTIONS OF PASTORAL LEADER
Toward the end of the sermon: bring out the ONE key point your sermon points to. Let's say the topic is conflict. Restate the main point in one sentence.	Musician comes forward AS pastor is restating the sermon in ONE sentence. Pastor invites congregation into time of silence
	Pastor "sets up" silence by saying something like, we're going to just think about how God is directing us to see ourselves and the condition of our own heart. Think about who in your life is very different than you and if they rub you the wrong way. Is God asking you for a different response to them? Let's see the question on the screen...
On screen comes the question: How is God asking you to think differently about people that rub you the wrong way?	Pastor continues: We're going to sit in silence for one minute. Our worship leader will time it, and I'll be praying and interceding for you the whole while. Let's listen for God
After one minute of timed silence, the music begins playing, either live or recorded, to transition to the next comments and worship leading instructions.	Pastor continues: We'd love to hear the thoughts of the community. It always encourages us. Pass your prayers on the written card, up front. Or just text what you want to say to the number on the screen.
Numbers go on the screen	Pastor reads texted prayers over music as they come in ...
Texting and reading ends	Pastor says, "We have heard the yearnings of the community of faith,"
	Background music stops, pastor sits, host in place
	Host makes an invitation to share offering, plus prayer
Offering while watching video or listening to a recording	Video ends, organist begins doxology, congregation stands
Doxology	Organist moves right into closing hymn or worship leader gets the band started for the closing song
Pastor / host / worship leader is prepared to reiterate invitation to connect after service, during this week, and at worship next week, figure eighteen	
benediction, closing music / postlude	

LIVE BAND-LED DISCIPLESHIP THREADS CHART

ACTION	TRANSITION
	Scrolling announcements over background music
	Band in place 5 minutes before start with countdown video
	Countdown at 0, band begins / lights dim
Three praise songs	Music starts
	People stand as music begins
	Spontaneous prayers during music without music stopping.
	May include a form of passing the peace
	At the end of the song, worship leader tells congregation to be seated
Video (testimony)	Begins immediately, no intro
Video ends, Welcome begins	Host is in place to welcome congregation
Welcome ends	Prayer for offering
	Video begins as offering begins
Video (thematic) and offering done	Pastor in place, lights come up
	Introduces self
	Moves into sermon after various connections
• Sermon, with prayer, texting, visuals woven in, • Reads scripture during sermon • May invite musician or someone else forward to help end the service	
Assignment, benediction, dismissal*	
Recorded music begins	

Things to notice about our chart

We have elected to show you the entire band-led service, so that you can get a feel for the importance of transitions. We will delve deeply into transitions in the next chapter. For now, notice the attention to inputting discipleship threads throughout the service. See the next chart on discipleship threads for both spoken-liturgy and live-band-led style services. If you are using an ancient-future hybrid, follow the spoken-liturgy pattern.

64

SPOKEN-LITURGY AND LIVE-BAND-LED
DISCIPLESHIP IMPACT OF AN INVITATIONAL ENDING

REINFORCING THE INVITE AT THE END	OPPORTUNITY FOR DISCIPLESHIP
… sermon, prayers, offering are completed	Guest has had an opportunity for God to soften his or her heart through the Word of God and interactive prayer*
… host or pastor is at the front. Music has stopped; host or pastor or worship leader says something like, Don't forget if you want to find out about the homeless shelter this week to go to the welcome center after worship. Also, next week we're going to be talking about fasting. We're sending you to the homeless shelter where people struggle sometimes to have a meal, and then we're coming back and asking you to intentionally give up food! Wonder what the connection is …	Guest can solidify thoughts about what he or she is going to get involved in this week and start thinking about next Sunday Action: As the pastor / host / worship leader talks about next week, put the title of the sermon up there with, perhaps, an image that identifies the sermon. If it's a different preacher than this week, state that.
…benediction Pastor, host or worship leader offers benediction	The call to discipleship is out there; the regulars and guest now have to choose.
background music starts up as people exit	Train greeters to connect with people on the way out as much as you did on their way in

WORSHIP TEAM DISCUSSION AND ACTION ITEMS

Which worship service format will you select for your church and why?

What do you need to change in your own life as spiritual leaders to be able to work with others on your team?

How do you plan to get started on developing a worship design team and a worship implementation team? Who will be on the team? What is your timeline for getting started?

How do you plan to get started on developing a sermon writing team? Who will be on the team? What is your timeline for getting started?

Phase Five: Artistry _____

Transitioning With Art & Passion

Regardless of whether you use the spoken-liturgy or the live-band-led style service, you will deal with similar transition issues for any group over 50 in number. We begin our Workbook discussion considering all the tools that are available to you in upfront worship leadership. These tools will help you offer smooth and potentially powerful transitions in your worship service. **CAVEAT:** Effective transitions are not just technical. They are spiritual. Do not try to adopt the technical side of transitions without the soul-work that goes with them.

Transitional prayers. At Accelerating Church, it's more than just the pastor that prays for the congregation. Upfront lay leaders and paid staff are taught to pray publicly as part of their public leadership. They are comfortable doing so because they are accountable to their own personal, spirited life of praise in their everyday lives with God as part of their leadership role. They have grown comfortable listening for and recognizing God's voice in their own lives and are able to apply that to upfront spiritual leadership. Before the service, during the service and even after the service they ask God to touch "my" heart as the leader so that "I" can lead others to this place of intimacy with God.

HOW TO USE PRAYER AS A TRANSITION TOOL

PLACES FOR PRAYER	THE TRANSITION
Before the call to worship (liturgy driven) or within the first song (band driven), to honor God's presence	Prayer of "praise"
The end of the welcome; pray for "us all" in the room to have open hearts	Prayer of "agreement."
The offering; to increase generosity from how we might be struggling to be generous	Prayer of confession "on behalf of others."
Before scripture; to understand what God is telling us	Prayer of "supplication"
During texting prayers, on for persons in seats to hear God	Prayer of "intercession"
Before leaving, Thanking God for being present.	Prayer of "thanksgiving"

Something to notice about the prayer-as-a-transition-tool chart.

If you are unfamiliar with different types of prayer, Google them. Teaching prayer in your church is a great pathway to discipleship. It stirs the hearts of persons in seats who are looking for that power connection. Use different forms of prayer during the service and then run discipleship classes on prayer for those that you are grooming to be part of a congregation wide prayer team.

Personal testimony.

We began in Chapter Five talking about the use of personal testimony. We hope you have grown your use of personal testimony in short sound-bites as you have been Building Worship Bridges these last months. Here are some more ways to use personal testimony as a transition tool to help you go deeper with persons in seats.

A BIT OF SELF REVELATION	TRANSITION
For example, let's say you have a liturgist reading a scripture passage. Is it about loss? The liturgist might say he's dealt with loss personally several times and it was always hard, but God was always true.	Helps persons in seats contextualize the reading of scripture that's about to come
Are you praying a prayer of confession for the congregation to be more generous? Include something about your own giving; in a few words ask God to grow you, or say you're grateful that God is encouraging you to grow generous.	Let's persons in seats hear that others struggle letting go of "stuff."
Are you praying at the end of the welcome? Mention briefly how God has strengthened you in the worship service along with the entire group.	Helps persons in seats get a feel for the power of the gathered community
Some place unplanned, most likely during the leading of a song, most often by the worship leader. You might say, "hallelujah," or "God we're so grateful," or something else. You say it because you're moved!	Allows persons in seats the opportunity to see how powerful the spirit is

Anticipate your role.

In 1950 having dead spots in a TV show or a program was not uncommon. In the 21st century, if there's a dead spot in your TV, computer or subscription radio, you immediately change the channel. When you have a dead spot in your worship service, persons in seats mentally change the channel. You do not get them back.

For the rest of your service, they are looking at their watch or playing games on their phones. Many worship services have dead spots due to lack of planning for transitions. Whether your style is spoken-liturgy or live-band-led, planning transitions might look like this:

HOW TO ANTICIPATE TRANSITIONS

ACTION	ANTICIPATION
FROM OPENING HYMN TO RESPONSIVE READING	Host moves to the mic during the last half of the last verse of the hymn
FROM THE RESPONSIVE READING TO PASSING THE PEACE	The host moves to the congregation to pass the peace; the organist begins playing the music for the hymn, the song leader moves to the mike to start singing approximately 15 seconds after the music starts
FROM THE SECOND HYMN TO THE WELCOME	Host moves to the mic during the last half of the last verse of the second hymn
FROM THE WELCOME TO THE VIDEO	The host cues the video and moves to his seat while the video is playing
FROM THE VIDEO TO THE SCRIPTURE READING	The reader moves into place and as the final sounds of the video are going and may begin talking over the final sounds of the video.

Start your part before the music ends.

You may have noticed in the last row in the above chart, the person reading scripture gets to her spot and begins introducing scripture before the video is done. If the choir was singing or the band was playing, you could do the same thing. The sound of the video or the reverberating chords from the organ can lend themselves to creating threads between segments.

If there is talking on the video at the end, then wait. But if it is music and the music is fading, you can begin. Live musicians can be intentional about holding a chord softly for the worship leader to begin speaking with music underneath.

HOW TO USE THE ENDING OF MUSIC OR VIDEOS TO CREATE TRANSITIONS

ACTION	ANTICIPATION
From the choir anthem or special music to the sermon	The pastor prays over the soft chords of the organ or piano
From the prayer to the initial interacting with the congregation	Music fades out during the prayer and pastor keeps going
From the message to the interactive prayer or whatever else might follow communion	If live music, the musician can begin playing softly at a point in the sermon or prayer time that you plan ahead of time

Reduce standing and sitting.

Standing endorses importance. The two most important times in the service are the beginning and the end because your guest will connect there (or not, depending on what you do!) Stand for the Praise, stand for the Dismissal and remain seated for the duration. You may also have the congregation stand during the reading of the Gospel. Compared to most liturgy-driven services, that is not much standing. Too much standing makes the service choppy and choppy worship makes experiencing God elusive.

USING STANDING AND SITTING AS TRANSITIONS

ACTION	WHAT TO SAY
Countdown video and background music end	Band or organist starts first song; over the music, the worship leader asks people to stand
Last hymn or song in the opening set	Host or other up front leader asks people to sit down
Scripture	Pastor or liturgist has people stand *May include congregation reading a verse or two together* after reading, worship leader says to be seated
Closing song, and remain standing throughout the rest of the service	Worship leader invites to stand; after song shares short announcements and dismissal

What to notice about our standing-sitting chart

The instructions to stand and sit are verbal, relational and personal, not a generic gesture. If you raise your arms up in the air to signal to people to stand up, they'll think you are the ref on the gridiron announcing a touchdown.

We often see choir directors "direct" the congregation in their singing by waving their arms as though the congregation is part of the choir. That would be a good thing to stop. It is not how our culture works. People will look at the screen and the lyrics and that will guide them. The upfront leader is a relatable person who is worshiping God and ushering persons in seats into God's presence, not conducting them into it.

Lighting

Lighting is an excellent transition tool. Consider the following chart:

HOW TO USE LIGHTING TRANSITIONS

WHERE TO USE LIGHTING TRANSITIONS	ACTION FOR LIGHTING TRANSITIONS
Announcements scrolling	Turn house lights down at the beginning
Scripture reading ended	Pastor or up front leader offers a prayer, lights come up
Sermon ended	Pastor or up front leader offers a prayer, to move congregation into prayer time and / or offering, house lights down
Dismissal	Background music starts, house lights completely up for exit

WORSHIP TEAM DISCUSSION QUESTIONS AND ACTION ITEMS

What did you learn about transitions in the workbook chapter on transitions and artistry?

What are you already doing in your church to make good transitions that engage people?

How can you improve transitions?

What else might you need to change besides technology to improve the overall flow and artistry of your service? Comment on:

- Developing the role of the host
- Dress code
- Personal spiritual practices
- A stronger sense of God's power in the worship service

What is your process and timeline for implementing changes?

Putting it all together

When we introduced the five segments of the worship service, we suggested that the real challenge is determining what fits under each of the five segments. Let us take a moment to consider one worship sequence.

A COMPLETE WORSHIP SERVICE

Worship Segments	What is under the Segment	Transition into and out of each segment	Time value
GATHERING	Announcements scrolling to back-ground music	Countdown video	About 20 minutes pre-service
PRAISE	Congregational singing, pass-ing the peace (optional) and a spoken or sung liturgy	Musical, verbal cue (please stand) and standing of the congregation Sitting down	About 10 minutes
PROCLAMATION	Scripture and sermon	Welcome and invitation Video that introduces sermon (at the beginning) Possible lighting change Pastoral prayer, music at the end, possible lighting change	About 30 minutes
RESPONSE	Interactive prayer, communion, offering, doxology (depending on style of service), congregational hymn / song	Music, verbal instructions into the prayer Stand after prayer for doxology, hymn, and / or dismissal	About 15 minutes
DISMISSAL	Reminder of invita-tion after worship, assignment, bene-diction	Recorded Background music, people moving out!	About 5 minutes

WORSHIP TEAM ACTION ITEMS

We are providing three charts to help you finalize your worship order. Select the one that you think will work best in your existing or new service. Our suggested sequence for each style is in the left-hand column. Insert your own revised order in the middle column of your preferred style and helpful transitions to make note of in the far right. Programs like Planning Center Online (PCO) will help you run transitions weekly.

THREE CHARTS FOR TRACKING WORSHIP ORDERS

Suggested Spoken-Liturgy	YOUR Spoke- Liturgy	HELPFUL TRANSITIONS
ANNOUNCEMENTS		
Opening Hymn		
Invitation to Worship		
(PASSING THE PEACE)		
Second Hymn		
WELCOME		
VIDEO		
Scripture		
MESSAGE		
INTERACTIVE PRAYER		
COMMUNION		
OFFERING		
DOXOLOGY		
CLOSING HYMN		
DISMISSAL		
POSTLUDE OR BACKGROUND MUSIC		

Suggested Live-Band Led	YOUR Live-Band-Led	HELPFUL TRANSITIONS
ANNOUNCEMENTS		
Two to three songs		
Welcome		
Video		
Message		
Dismissal / Benediction		
Closing song		

Suggested Ancient Future	YOUR Ancient Future	HELPFUL TRANSITIONS
ANNOUNCEMENTS		
BELL		
LITURGY		
HYMN		
PASSING THE PEACE		
PRAISE SONG		
WELCOME		
VIDEO		
MESSAGE		
INTERACTIVE PRAYER		
CREED		
COMMUNION		
OFFERING		
DOXOLOGY		
CLOSING HYMN		
DISMISSAL, BENEDICTION		
RECORDED MUSIC		

Additional Resources

Contact information:

Consultant / Coaches / Friends / Connections

Cathy Townley
www.townleycoaching.com

Kay Kotan
www.kaykotan.com

Bishop Robert Farr
Resident Bishop of The Missouri Annual Conference
of The United Methodist Church

Building Worship Bridges: Construction Guide
For additional copies of this workbook, visit:

www.marketsquarebooks.com

To get updates and training opportunities for *Building Worship Bridges,* head to the website:

www.BuildingWorshipBridges.com"

Our Top SEVENTY-SIX Pick of Opening
and Second Hymns

As noted in the Book Building Worship Bridges, many hymns in most denominational hymnals are not singable if you do not know them already. Some church people know the tunes to numerous hymns and they still cannot sing them. If songs are singable, new people catch on to them right away. If they are not singable, new people just stand and stare. We want new people to fit in! There are enough hymns in most denominational hymnals that church regulars enjoy singing and that new people can learn quickly that we do not have to include the hymns with meandering melodies and difficult ranges. Some new people will remember the old standard hymns from their childhood if they grew up in the church. That will help them participate.

We have organized our list into three categories. Category one is opening hymns, which must have strength, power and energy. We selected songs for this category based on the normally upbeat tempo of the hymn. Category two is hymns that could be opening hymns or second hymns. These songs could be played with faster or slower tempo and still have impact. Category three is hymns that work best as a second hymn because they are more mellow than those in the opening hymn list. If you are going to follow a spoken liturgy model or a live-band led model and you want to string a couple hymns (or hymns and contemporary praise songs) together, this list will help you determine which ones to use and where to use them.

You can use these hymns in various combinations in your worship service throughout the year (during the holidays, you would use seasonal hymns). You can also add to this list with hymns that your congregation especially likes that we might not know or that we eliminated from our choices. Remember: you do not need to feel obligated to use every hymn in the hymnal during a calendar year. There is no need to feel guilty about not using some of the hymns in the hymnal – ever!

We have selected the following hymns from the United Methodist Hymnal. Most are songs that are found in multiple denominational hymnals, with a few exceptions.

OPENING HYMNS (first lines)
1. All Glory, Laud and Honor
2. All Hail the Power of Jesus' Name
3. And Can it Be that I should Gain
4. Blessed Assurance
5. Come Thou Long Expected Jesus
6. Come, ye thankful people, come
7. Crown him with many crowns
8. Do Lord, Remember Me
9. For all the saints, who from these labors rest
10. Go tell it on the mountain
11. God of Grace and God of glory
12. Holy, Holy, Holy Lord God Almighty
13. How Great Thou Art
14. I sing the almighty power of God
15. Immortal, Invisible, God only wise
16. Joyful, joyful we adore thee
17. Lift up your heads, ye mighty gates
18. Majesty, worship his majesty
19. Mine eyes have seen the Glory
20. Oh, For a thousand tongues to sing
21. Oh happy day that fixed my choice
22. Oh Zion haste
23. Onward, Christian soldiers
24. Shall we gather at the river

25. Soon and very soon

26. Swing low, sweet chariot

27. We've a story to tell to the nations

28. What a fellowship, what a joy divine

29. When the storms of life are raging

OPENING OR SECOND HYMNS

1. A mighty fortress is our God

2. Amazing Grace! How sweet the sound

3. Be thou my vision (try the Rend Collective version some time!)

4. Blessed be the name (UM Hymnal, not the praise song by the same name!)

5. Come Thou Fount of Every Blessing (try the Sufjan Stevens arrangement some time!)

6. Come Ye Faithful raise the strain

7. Go down Moses

8. Hymn of Promise

9. I want to walk as a child of the light

10. Let there be peace on earth

11. Nothing but the blood

12. O God our help in ages past

13. What a friend we have in Jesus

SECOND HYMNS

1. Abide with me

2. All to Jesus I surrender

3. Alleluia

4. And God will raise you up on Eagle's wings

5. Be present at our table Lord

6. Beneath the cross of Jesus

7. Blest be the tie that binds

8. Chidren of the Heavenly Father

9. Dona nobis pacem

10. Fairest Lord Jesus, ruler of all nature

11. Faith of our fathers

12. Great is thy faithfulness

13. He leadeth me O Blessed thought

14. Here I am Lord

15. I love to tell the story

16. Jesus, joy of our desiring

17. Just as I am without one plea

18. Lord, I want to be a Christian

19. Nearer my God to thee

20. Nobody knows the trouble I've seen

21. Old Rugged Cross

22. Stand by me

23. Surely the presence of the Lord is in this place

24. Take my life, and let it be consecrated

25. There is a balm in Gilead

26. This is my father's world

27. Thy word is a lamp unto my feet

28. Trust and obey

29. Turn your eyes upon Jesus

30. We are climbing Jacob's ladder

31. We shall overcome

32. When peace like a river attendeth my soul

33. When I survey the wondrous cross

34. To God be the Glory!

You can combine these hymns with praise songs that you find on the next page.

Finding Singable Praise Songs

As with denominational hymnal hymns, many contemporary praise songs are very difficult for the average person in seats to sing. Even musical praise groups and choirs have trouble singing them. Cathy has done a Google search to find the top 100 praise songs, and saw the CCLI list. Cathy approves! Some of the songs on the list date back several years, and they are still included in a current list. Google "top 100 praise songs of _____". Insert "this year" in the blank space.

As you listen through the songs you find, learn to hear first, second and third songs. In most cases, it is important to start your Praise Segment with energy, that is, with an "upbeat" song. Many songs on the top 100 list are powerful first songs to sing. If you are doing three songs, then the second song can be upbeat like the first, and the third one would be slower and more meditative. Or, you can do a first song that is upbeat, a second song that is slower and meditative, and a third song that is more upbeat. Learn to create flow!

They key factor in making them sound good is to mimic the recording of the song as closely as possible. If you do not have all the instruments represented with talent and skill (people in your church who can play those instruments), learn to use loops or strip down the sound. See our workbook chapter on how to make music a WOW.

Searching for artists

The other search to learn to do is to find songs from artists you really like that may represent a specific genre of music. Some musical categories we might not think about are country, blue-grass and what some might call an "indy" sound. Additionally, you might wish to find standard gospel tunes and praise songs as well as contemporary R&B praise songs.

Cathy has called upon some of her millennial musical friends to find artists that represent a few of these categories for you to begin to explore:[5]

Country and blue grass contemporary Christian sounds:
All Sons and Daughters
Rend Collective

"Indy" artists (Indy "sounding" artists):
Welcome Wagon
Listener
David Bazan
Josh Cleveland

Artists that are in the "Christian" scene:
Gungor
Jenny & Tyler
John Mark McMillan
Jon Foreman
Wayfarer

Artists that are in the secular scene who are also Christians:
Sufjan Stevens
Mutemath

R&B Praise Artists
Kirk Franklin
Mary Mary
sometimes Kanye West
sometimes Common

---

[5] Many thanks to church planters Cullen Tanner, Jeremiah Lideen and Shawn Moore. U guys r the bomb.

TEN CONSTRUCTION PRINCIPLES

FOR BUILDING WORSHIP BRIDGES

Tell God's Story

Tell Your Story

Pay Attention to First Impressions

Pay Attention to Quality

Enliven the First Ten Minutes

Enliven Spiritual Practices

Strengthen the Ending

Strengthen Design Processes

Run Transitions

Run the Race

We invite you to tear out this page and put it on your office wall or some other place to remind yourself what Building Worship Bridges is really all about!

Other books from
Market Square Books

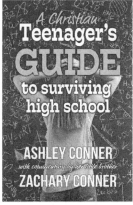

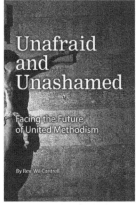

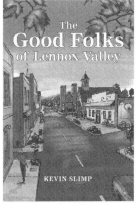

A Christian Teenager's Guide
To Surviving High School
Ashley Conner & Zachary Conner

Unafraid and Unashamed
Facing the Future of United Methodism
Wil Cantrell

The Good Folks
of Lennox Valley
Kevin Slimp

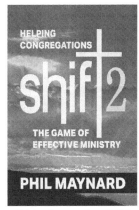

Understanding Your Call
Through the Eyes of 11 Biblical Figures

Helping Congregations Shift 2
the Game of Effective Ministry
Phil Maynard

marketsquarebooks.com

72869961R00053

Made in the USA
Middletown, DE
09 May 2018